Penguin Books 1660

The Lovers   Raymond Peynet

To Vic and Moyra
from Mike
Christmas 1962.

D1351104

Raymond Peynet

The Lovers

Penguin Books

Penguin Books Ltd, Harmondsworth, Middlesex
AUSTRALIA: Penguin Books Pty, Ltd, 762 Whitehorse Road, Mitcham, Victoria

The Lovers' Pocketbook (1954), *The Lovers' Travelogue* (1955),
The Lovers' Bedside Book (1956), *The Lovers' Keepsake* (1958), and
The Lovers' Weekend Book (1959) first published by Perpetua

This selection first published in Penguin Books 1962

Made and printed in Great Britain
by Hazell Watson & Viney Ltd, Aylesbury and Slough
Set in Monotype Garamond

Peynet

*M*ost appropriately last Spring in Paris, during the State Visit of Her Majesty, *entente cordiale* was additionally cemented with the official presentation to the Queen, by the Ville de Paris, of twelve dolls for Princess Anne, designed by Peynet and representing characters from his cartoons. It is a measure of their affection for Peynet that the French chose him as a representative on this gay occasion.

The success of Peynet in this country has been nothing short of meteoric. Up to four years ago he was very much a sacred preserve of the French and known to few people outside that traditional paradise of Lovers. And understandably so, for the theme of Peynet's work embraces (one might say) almost exclusively the unlimited variations of which the female anatomy is capable. Like a true Frenchman, Peynet never tires of exploring its infinite possibilities. In his hands the heart takes wings and a bosom speaks volumes, and it is little wonder that the French felt that this was purely a field for the connoisseur. *The Lovers' Pocketbook* broke through the barrier and finally disproved the libel that the English are a Cold Race.

Far from being a clumsy adventurer, Peynet approaches his dedicated field with the delicacy of a poet. Through the exploits of his unique lovers, the *Poète* and his *Fiancée*, we share a world of innocent delights and fantasies.

Maybe everyday love is not like this – but this is the way we like to think it is: gay, frank, openhearted and slightly four-dimensional. And in case you think we are over-biased in Peynet's favour, let us quote evidence of most remarkable accord in Fleet Street: 'Deliciously absurd and delicately indelicate' SUNDAY TIMES; 'Unique' THE OBSERVER; 'A charm to give to anyone' NEW STATESMAN; 'Surrealist, gay, attractive' PUNCH; and if that is not enough, 'Utterly delightful' DAILY HERALD. Love, unlike politics, knows no barriers!   *Ronald Searle, 1958*

'Huh! Is she afraid someone will steal him?'

'Do you remember that sunset in Capri, darling?'

Love Birds

7. Peynet.

'Oh darling, I never knew you had it in you'

'Well *you* said this was a love nest'

Peynet

'Let me come too, darling! I won't take up much room'

'Really! I think you've got love on the brain'

'Mother – he doesn't *trust* me!'

'Mi, mi, la, sol, si, fa, re ...'

'I can't swim'

'Here you are Sir. Two and a half to the Canaries'

'Spring! – '

'Spring-a-ling-aling! Spring-a-ling-aling!'

'Don't mind Mummy – she's a bit old-fashioned'

'If you ask me he's only half in love with her'

Peynet

'That one *really* puts his heart into his love letters'

Nest-class Sleepers

'I'm a fishmonger'
'And I'm a typist in a flower shop'

Lover's Reckoning

'Still angry, darling?'

r.Peynet

7. Peynet

'No, *you* choose'

'I couldn't wait, so I came to meet you!'

'You make me feel I can trust you …'

I've a little bit tucked away which will help us to be happy!'

Peynet

'It's Monsieur and Madame Salvador Dali'

'Honestly, I promise I'll come back next year'

'Denise will be down in a minute, she's in the shower'

'I don't know *how* you manage
to get these holes in your guitars ...'

'Yes, he lives in a little world of his own'

'Darling, why don't you come out of your shell'

'My dear, she's an absolute pearl'

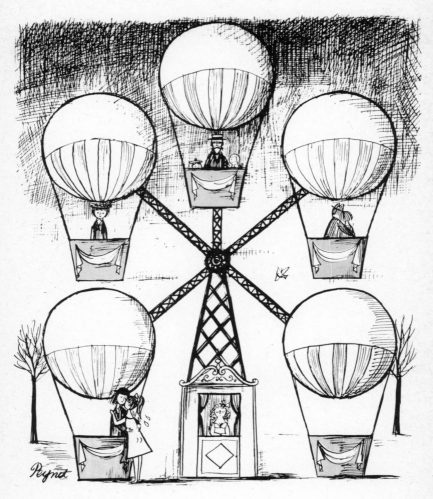

'Promise you'll come back …'

'3D glasses, explanatory booklets, aspirin ...'

'Hurry, darling, it's ticking up!'

Peynet

'I work in a greengrocers – what do you do?'

'Just a short business trip, darling'

'Oh dear, have I kept you waiting?'

La Ronde

'Which do you prefer, dearest?'

'Look! The Low Countries!'

'My hands get cold ...'

'Oh *why* did you do it when I loved you so?

'Toys – that way, Sir!'

'But he won't get his sea-legs like that!'

'The Danes always "say it with flowers"'

'Nothing like a steam bath for reducing'

Kipper factory

Peynet

Fishing for compliments

'Fire!'

ı. Peynet

Pipe Dreams

'Well, it isn't everyday one gets the chance
of meeting the God of Love!'

'I know, Mama .... I *expected* a poet to be different but ...'

- Stowaways -

'All change for the Interior'

'… and I've two delightful little knick-knacks just inside,
if you would care to see them.'

'You mark my words – he's having an affair with the florist'

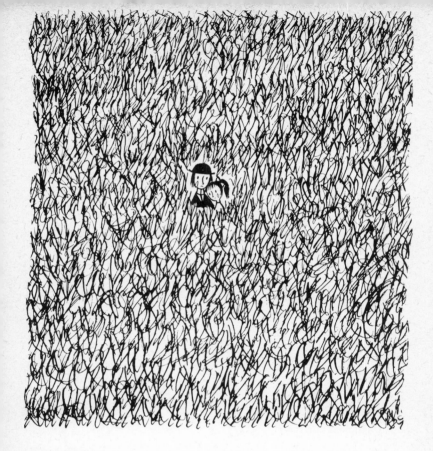

THE BUSH
'If only I had a rubber, I'd get us out of here'

'Ah! Spring ...'

'Well, I couldn't *help* dropping him'

'Must we do *all* of the Ivory Coast on foot?'

Peynet

The day the postman called

THOUSAND AND ONE NIGHTS
'Er, would you send up 2 large white coffees,
20 croissants, 30 brioches, 40 pieces of toast,
2 pounds of butter, and 10 pots of jam?'

'Operator! I asked for REGENT, not PRIMROSE'

'If *you* were more obliging,
  I wouldn't need to ask the neighbours for help'

'The management of the Hotel Escargot
wishes you a pleasant night'

'Yes sweetheart, I'll save you from your dreadful dream
– if you'll tell me where you put the key ...'

The Poet

'And what's more, it's cruel to keep animals in a little house!'

'Ah chérie, I have suffered so much'

'How lucky we called him Johann'

U.S.A.
Lift Strike

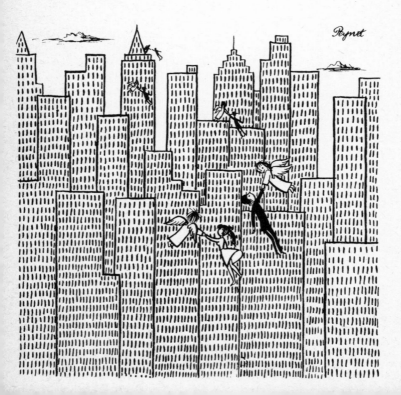

'Let's hurry. It's started already ...'

Peynet

'How many minks to a coat, sweetie?'

'Oh, *him* – he's crazy about me'

Peynet

Peynet

'If you say goodbye to everyone, we'll be here all winter'

'Darling, I wish you wouldn't
 keep giving me these melting glances'

'Still cross, dearest?'

'Still angry, darling?'

'When *will* you come down to earth!'

School for Lovers

'BRUTE!'

'I'm bored ...'

'You must do better than that if you want to be a nightingale,
Miss Nightingale'

'She loves me she loves me not she loves me
she loves me not she loves ...'

'Been waiting long, darling?'

'Silly to part for ever, just for a tiff'

'The engine driver's forgotten his lines!'

Thin end of the wedge

'Good heavens! 85 in the shade'

'But Professor, you are not *nearly* on the note!'

'But you told me to come as I was'

'Do take a chair – my husband will be down in a moment'

'Darling I must ring off, I've got something on the boil'

'I never dreamt our love could reach such heights'

'You're homesick – I can see it in your eyes!'

'Could you all Adore a little more quietly, please'

Pupnet